25 Instant & Irresistible

Math Board Games

Reproducible Games That Teach Essential Math Skills
Including Multiplication, Fractions, Time, Money & More
by Mary Beth Spann

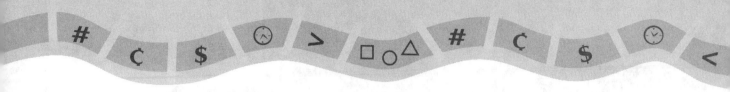

Dedication

To my family...and to teachers everywhere who empower children by helping them master mathematics.

—M.B.S.

Acknowledgments

Great thanks to editors Liza Charlesworth and Cindi Mitchell, who made these games sparkle; and to artist, James Hale, and designer, Pamela Simmons, who made them shine!

Edited by Cindi Mitchell
Cover and interior design by Pamela Simmons
Illustration by James Hale

ISBN: 0-590-28212-3.

Table of Contents

Introduction 5

Why Include Math Games in Your Curriculum? 6

Constructing the Math Games 7

Introducing the Math Games 8

Creating a Math Game Center 9

Skills Matrix 10

The Math Games

Master Detective . . . . *(place value)* 11

Super Sleuth . . . . *(place value)* 14

On a Roll . . . . *(addition)* 17

Double Trouble . . . . *(place value, addition)* 19

Skee-Ball! . . . . *(place value, addition)* 21

Rolling Addition . . . . *(place value, addition)* 24

The Number Hop . . . . *(addition, subtraction)* 26

Bubble Up! . . . . *(addition, subtraction)* 28

Snake Around . . . . *(subtraction)* 30

Mice Multiplication . . . . *(multiplication)* 32

Multiplication Tic-Tac-Toe . . . *(multiplication, logic)* 34

Cookie Quotients . . . . *(division)* 36

Fraction Action . . . . *(fractions, logic)* 38

Guess-timation! . . . . *(estimation, counting)* 41

Put On a Happy Face . . . . *(geometric shapes)* 43

Ms. Peabody's Bank . . . . *(place value, addition, money)* . . . 44

Carnival Cash . . . . *(addition, subtraction, money)* . . 46

Time Flies! . . . . *(telling time)* 49

Measure Up . . . . *(measurement, logic)* 52

Great Graph Race . . . . *(addition, graphing)* 54

Constellation Graph . . . . *(graphing)* 56

Forget-Me-Not . . . . *(visual memory, counting)* 58

Button, Button . . . . *(logic)* 60

Spider Trap . . . . *(logic)* 62

Get Even! . . . . *(logic, counting)* 64

Introduction

Welcome to *25 Instant & Irresistible Math Board Games*. On these pages you'll find an enjoyable collection of reproducible games to make learning mathematics exciting and challenging in your primary classroom. The games are carefully developed to provide students with opportunities to practice basic skills, develop reasoning strategies, test theories, and apply mathematical concepts while having fun!

At the top of each game's directions page, you'll find a list of skills that game targets. Next to the game's title, you'll find the recommended number of players. Also included on each of these pages is a list telling exactly what supplies you'll need to get started.

You do not need to buy extra materials to play these games. Most of the activities require using only the game chips and number cubes (red, yellow) that are packaged with this book. Other supplies such as construction paper, pencils, and crayons are probably already in your classroom.

The games in this book are designed to follow math lessons presented in formal teacher-directed settings. Because game playing in and of itself requires students to organize and direct their own learning, students will be most successful playing the games in this collection after they have been introduced to the skills and concepts imbedded in each one. The Skills Matrix, provided on page 10, allows you to see at a glance which skills each game reinforces.

Why Include Math Games in Your Curriculum?

Games will enhance your math curriculum in many ways. They provide:

⬇ an opportunity for students to play cooperatively with other students.

⬇ a chance for students to test and apply the math skills and concepts that they've mastered in more formal math assignments.

⬇ an informal assessment tool to help you determine whether students are able to recall and apply math skills in a real-life recreational setting.

⬇ an opportunity for students to communicate with other people about math concepts.

The NCTM Standards encourage teachers to actively involve students in mathematics through interactive hands-on learning by providing opportunities to explore, develop, test, and discuss mathematical concepts. These games provide an ideal setting to meet those goals.

Constructing the Math Games

Materials you will need:

- copies of the game boards and corresponding directions
- copies of game cards (if applicable)
- letter-size folders (one per game)
- 6 x 9 manila envelopes (for those games that require game cards)
- scissors
- glue
- crayons or markers
- clear self-sticking adhesive paper or laminating material (optional)

1 After deciding which game you want to make, cut out the game and the corresponding directions.

2 For those games that require the reproducible game cards, consider mounting the cards on construction paper or oaktag and covering them with clear adhesive or laminate before cutting apart. For each game, be sure to make several sets of cards.

3 Use markers or crayons to color in the game board as desired. (Tip: You may wish to have students decorate games for you, but caution them not to use dark colors over directions or game details.)

4 Open a file folder and lay flat. Glue the directions to the left-hand side and the game board to the right-hand side.

5 Label the folder's tab with the game's name. You may also want to label the front of the folder.

6 After the game has been colored, glued in place, and labeled, cover the whole file folder with clear self-sticking adhesive or laminate material.

7 If the game has game cards, glue a 6 x 9 manila envelope to the outside of the file folder. Place the game cards inside the envelope.

8 Place the file folders in a file caddy (available at most office supply stores) and store the collection in your Math Game Center.

Introducing the Math Games

The following steps will help support students' efforts to play the math games on their own.

1 Make certain children are comfortable with the math skills presented in each game. Review these skills ahead of time, if necessary.

2 Take the time to play each game with the students.

3 Be sure that students understand how to use the materials and that they can understand and follow the directions.

4 Walk students through your math game storage system.

Creating a Math Game Center

The math games in this book can be part of a larger Math Game Center. Here are tips for setting up such a center.

Reserve a special corner of your classroom for a Math Game Center. Try to arrange it near a bulletin board so you can use it to display interactive math-related games and information, such as graphs, diagrams, and so on.

The bulletin board can also be used to display sign-up sheets to keep track of how many students have completed each activity.

Enlist children's help in decorating the center. Prepare a schedule so that two or three children at a time are responsible for helping you rotate materials on a biweekly basis.

Send a letter inviting parents to lend math-related games from home. In your letter, cite the importance of including games in your curriculum.

Ask friends and colleagues to lend you math games and manipulatives.

Collect teacher resource materials with game ideas and reproducible manipulatives.

Think of creative ways to present and organize math games. For example, try creating a math game cube. Find a sturdy cube-shaped box. Fold in the flaps at one end and place that end on the floor. Glue game boards to the remaining five sides. To play the games, children sit on the floor or on cushions around the box. Game pieces may be stored in manila envelopes attached to the inside of the box.

Skills Matrix

	Place Value	Addition	Subtraction	Multiplication	Division	Fractions	Estimation	Geometric Shapes	Money	Telling Time	Measurement	Graphing	Visual Memory	Logical Reasoning	Counting
Master Detective	●														
Super Sleuth	●														
On a Roll		●													
Double Trouble	●	●													
Skee-Ball!	●	●													
Rolling Addition	●	●												●	
The Number Hop		●	●												
Bubble Up!		●	●											●	
Snake Around			●											●	●
Mice Multiplication				●											
Multiplication Tic-Tac-Toe				●										●	
Cookie Quotients					●										
Fraction Action						●								●	
Guess-timation!							●								●
Put On a Happy Face								●							
Ms. Peabody's Bank	●	●							●						
Carnival Cash		●	●						●						
Time Flies!										●					
Measure Up											●			●	
Great Graph Race		●										●			
Constellation Graph												●			
Forget-Me-Not													●		●
Button, Button														●	
Spider Trap														●	
Get Even!														●	●

Master Detective

Any number can play

How to Win The first person to cover up all of his shaded numbers is the winner.

How to Play

1 Players each personalize cards by using a light-colored crayon to shade in any five numbers on their game board.

2 The caller, or master detective, places the clue cards in a bag or shoe box and selects one clue card at a time and reads aloud the word clues. The caller does not read the number in the magnifying glass.

3 The players listen to the clues carefully and try to find the mystery numbers on their game boards. They place chips only when the answer corresponds to a shaded number on their board.

4 The first player to cover up all of his or her shaded numbers shouts, "Stop!" That player then reads the numbers back to the caller to see if he or she won the game. The winner is the new master detective and will become the next caller.

What You Need

❖ game boards
   (1 for each player)

❖ clue cards
   (cut apart)

❖ chips

❖ crayons

❖ paper bag or
   shoe box

Master Detective

I have one ten and zero ones. **10**	I have two tens and zero ones. **20**	I have two tens and eight ones. **28**	I have one ten and five ones. **15**
I have two tens and one one. **21**	I have two tens and five ones. **25**	I have five tens and four ones. **54**	I have six tens and seven ones. **67**
I have one ten and three ones. **13**	I have seven tens and three ones. **73**	I have one ten and seven ones. **17**	I have three tens and one one. **31**
I have seven tens and six ones. **76**	I have three tens and seven ones. **37**	I have four tens and five ones. **45**	I have five tens and one one. **51**
I have eight tens and two ones. **82**	I have nine tens and six ones. **96**	I have six tens and nine ones. **69**	I have one ten and two ones. **12**

Master Detective

Game Board

Name

Super Sleuth

Any number can play

How to Win The first person to cover up all of his shaded numbers is the winner.

How to Play

1 Players each personalize cards by using a light-colored crayon to shade in any five numbers on their game board.

2 The caller, or super sleuth, places the clue cards in a bag or shoe box and selects one clue card at a time and reads aloud the word clues. The caller does not read the number in the magnifying glass.

3 The players listen to the clues carefully and try to find the mystery numbers on their game boards. They place chips only when the answer corresponds to a shaded number on their board.

4 The first player to cover up all of his or her shaded numbers shouts, "Stop!" That player then reads the numbers back to the caller to see if he or she won the game. The winner is the new super sleuth and will become the next caller.

What You Need

- ❖ game boards (*1 for each player*)
- ❖ clue cards (*cut apart*)
- ❖ chips
- ❖ crayons
- ❖ paper bag or shoe box

Super Sleuth

I have two hundreds, zero tens, and seven ones. **207**	I have two hundreds, one ten, and seven ones. **217**	I have seven hundreds, two tens, and six ones. **726**	I have one hundred, zero tens, and zero ones. **100**
I have four hundreds, one ten, and one one. **411**	I have eight hundreds, six tens, and nine ones. **869**	I have five hundreds, five tens, and one one. **551**	I have seven hundreds, two tens, and one one. **721**
I have nine hundreds three tens, and six ones. **936**	I have four hundreds, nine tens, and three ones. **493**	I have one hundred, one ten, and four ones. **114**	I have three hundreds, six tens, and nine ones. **369**
I have three hundreds, nine tens, and six ones. **396**	I have one hundred, four tens, and one one. **141**	I have nine hundreds, three tens, and four ones. **934**	I have nine hundreds, four tens, and three ones. **943**
I have three hundreds, nine tens, and four ones. **394**	I have six hundreds, three tens, and nine ones. **639**	I have five hundreds, one ten, and five ones. **515**	I have nine hundreds, six tens, and eight ones. **968**

Super Sleuth

Name

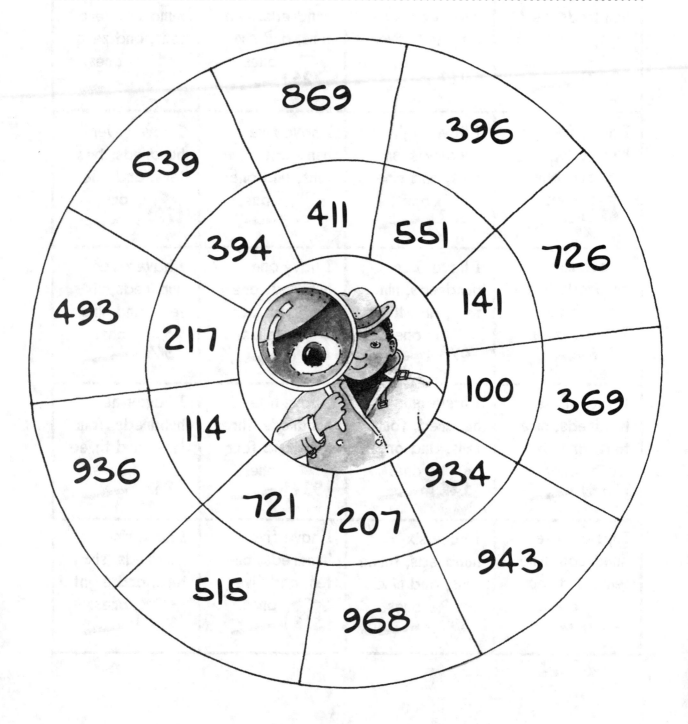

16

On a Roll... 2 Players

How to Win   The player with the lowest score at the end of the game is the winner

How to Play

What You Need

- game boards
  (1 for each player)
- 2 number cubes
- chips

1 Each player rolls the number cube. The player with the largest number goes first.

2 Each player takes a turn rolling the two cubes and adding the two numbers together.

3 The player then uses chips to cover up one, two, but no more than three numbers that when added equal the total number on the cubes. For example, if a player's number cubes total 12, she or he may choose to cover up 2 and 10; or 3, 4, and 5; or any other combination that totals 12.

4 The players continue taking turns rolling the cubes and covering up numbers until the total rolled cannot be found. They may *not* use just one of the numbers rolled.

5 Each player then adds together his or her remaining uncovered numbers and the total becomes that player's score.

6 The winner is the player with the lowest score.

On a Roll

Name

18

Double Trouble

2 to 4 Players

How to Win The player with the highest score at the end of the game is the winner.

How to Play

1 Each player rolls one number cube. The player with the largest number goes first.

2 Players take turns rolling both number cubes, using the record sheet to keep a running total of the numbers rolled. The yellow cube represents the ones place and the red cube represents the tens place.

3 If a player rolls doubles (for example, a 2 and a 2), he or she must place zeros on the record sheet for that roll.

4 Play continues until each player records ten rolls. The player with the highest score wins.

What You Need

- 1 record sheet
- 1 yellow cube (*representing ones place numbers*)
- 1 red cube (*representing tens place numbers*)

Double Trouble

	Player 1:	Player 2:
Roll #1		
Roll #2		
Subtotal		
Roll #3		
Subtotal		
Roll #4		
Subtotal		
Roll #5		
Subtotal		
Roll #6		
Subtotal		
Roll #7		
Subtotal		
Roll #8		
Subtotal		
Roll #9		
Subtotal		
Total		

Skee-Ball! .... 2 Players

How to Win The person with the highest score at the end of the game wins.

How to Play

What You Need

- 1 game board
- record sheets *(1 for each player)*
- pencils
- chips
- 1 number cube

1 Players share one game board. Each player selects a record sheet and rolls. Largest number goes first.

2 Players take turns rolling the cube. To determine the place value of the number, player places a chip in the HOME box and uses fingers to very gently snap it down the "lane" so it lands in one of the spaces marked "Ones," "Tens," or "Hundreds." (Tip: It's a good idea to place the game board against a wall or a standing hardcover book, so the chip will not fly off the game board.)

3 The player records the number on the record sheet. (For example, if a player rolls a 3 on the number cube and then snaps the chip to the circle marked "Hundreds," the player then records the number 3 in the "Hundreds" space on record sheet.)

4 If the chip lands in a space that indicates a place value column on the record sheet that is filled (only two possible) the player must pass turn to the other player. If the chip does not land in any space or lands on a line, the player may keep trying.

5 Play continues until players have each filled in all six spaces on their record sheet. Players add up their scores and the player with the highest score is the winner.

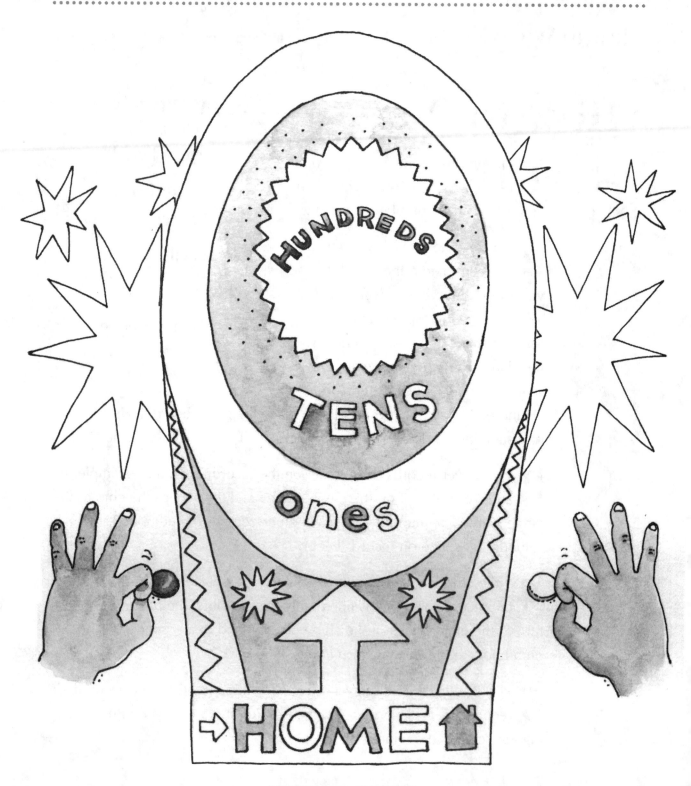

Skee-Ball!

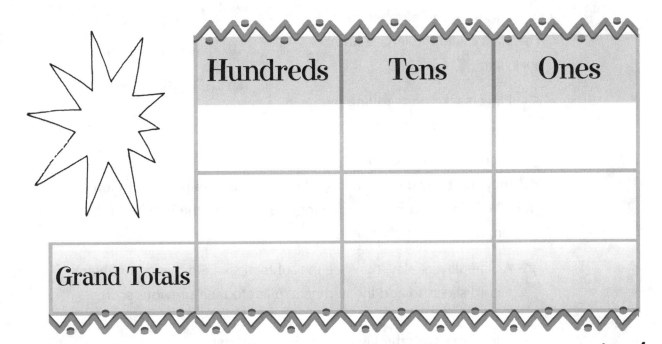

Record Sheet

Name

Record each roll in one of the spaces below. Add the two numbers together and find your grand total.

	Hundreds	Tens	Ones
Grand Totals			

Rolling Addition .... Any number can play

How to Win The player with the largest sum at the end of the game is the winner.

How to Play

What You Need

- record sheets
  (1 for each player)
- 1 number cube
- pencils

1 Each player takes record sheet and rolls one number cube. The player with the largest number goes first.

2 Players take turns rolling the number cube three times.

3 Each time players roll the die, they must decide whether to place that number in the "Hundreds," "Tens," or "Ones" column. Once they've recorded the number in a column, they cannot change it.

4 As the players play, they use the subtotal space provided on their record sheets to add the numbers rolled to their previous scores.

5 The player with the largest sum is the winner.

Another Way to Play The player with the smallest sum is the winner.

Rolling Addition

Name

	Hundreds	Tens	Ones
Turn 1			
Turn 2			
Subtotal			
Turn 3			
Subtotal			
Turn 4			
Total			

The Number Hop .... 2 to 4 Players

How to Win The first player to reach the end of the bunny trail is the winner.

How to Play

1 Players place their game markers on START and decide who will go first.

2 Players take turns rolling two number cubes.

3 Players look at the numbers on the cubes and double the value of the cube that has the highest number. (If they roll doubles, they may roll again.) They then move their chip ahead that number of spaces.

4 Players then look at the lowest number rolled and move their chip back that number of spaces.

5 Play continues until one person comes to the end of the bunny trail and is declared the winner. (Players do not have to roll an exact number to exit the board.)

Another Way to Play After five turns, the player who is the farthest along the bunny trail is the winner.

What You Need

- game board
- 2 number cubes
- chips *(each player chooses a different color for a game marker)*

The Number Hop

Game Board

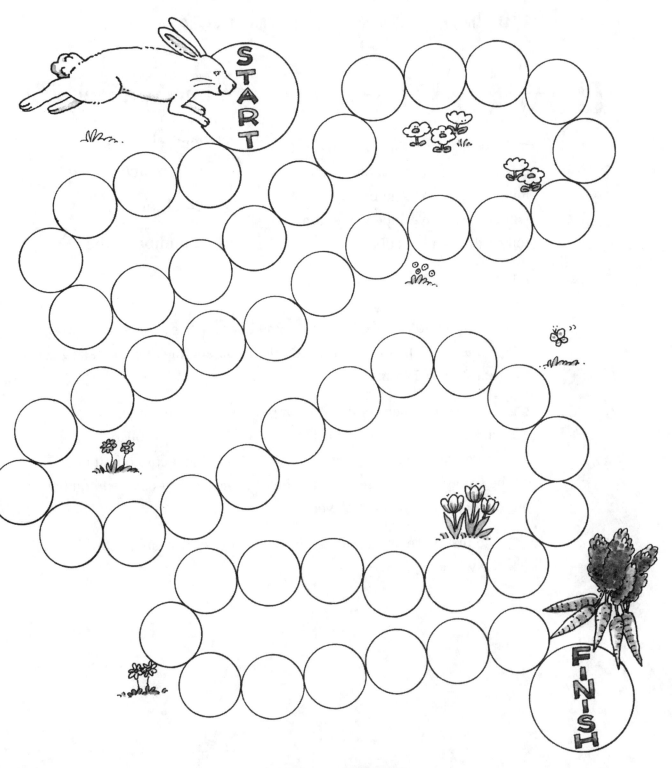

Bubble Up!....................................2 Players

How to Win The first player to lift all the chips from his game board is the winner.

How to Play

What You Need

- game boards *(1 for each player)*
- 24 chips
- 2 number cubes

1 Players each place a chip on all numbered "bubbles" on their game board, and decide who will go first. Players then take turns rolling the number cubes.

2 With each roll, a player has two choices in determining which number to remove from the game board. *For example,* if a player rolls a 2 and a 5, he or she may: **add the numbers together to make 7, or subtract 2 from 5 to make 3.**

3 Players must then remove the chip from the number decided upon and then explain their reasoning. (Example: "I rolled a 2 and a 5 so I'm adding them together to make 7. I'm lifting a chip off number 7 on the game board.") If neither number matches a chip-covered number, play moves on to the next player.

4 The first player to lift all the chips from her or his game board is the winner.

Bubble Up!

Game Board

Name

29

**Teaches
This Skill**
One-digit
Subtraction

Snake Around .... 2 Players

How to Win The first player to form an unbroken line of chips from one side of the game board to the other is the winner.

How to Play

1 Players decide who will go first and where to begin. One player will begin on the "start" at the top of the game board and go down; the other on the "start" on the right-hand side of the game board and go across.

2 Players take turns rolling two number cubes. They subtract the smallest number from the largest number to find the difference. (If a player rolls doubles, he or she may roll again.) They then collect that number of chips and place them one after another in the squares on the game board, connecting them to the starting chip. The line formed by the chips does not have to be straight, but there can be no skipped boxes or diagonal moves.

3 If a player comes to roadblock where the other player's chips block the path, she or he must go around that player's path.

4 The first player to form an unbroken line of chips from one side of the game board to the other side is the winner.

What You Need

- 1 game board
- 2 number cubes
- 20 chips per player (*each player chooses one color*)

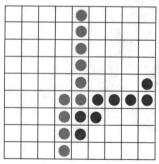

The player with the light chips is the winner

Snake Around

Game Board

Mice Multiplication

Any number can play

How to Win The first player to color all of his or her mice is the winner.

How to Play

1 Each player takes one game board.

2 Each player rolls one cube. The player with the largest number goes first.

3 The first player rolls both cubes. The numbers on the cubes represent factors to be multiplied. (For example, if a player rolls a 3 and a 4, multiply 3 x 4 = 12.)

4 After finding the answer, the player will color that number of mice on his or her game board. (In the example above, the player will color 12 mice.) Player may use a different color crayon for each turn.

5 The first player to color in all of her or his mice is the winner. Players must color the exact number of mice to win.

Another Way to Play Cover each mouse with a colored chip. Follow the same directions as above, but instead of having players color the mice, have players remove that number of chips from their game board. The first player to remove all the chips from the game board is the winner. The player must take away the exact number of chips to win.

What You Need

- ♦ game boards *(1 for each player)*
- ♦ crayons
- ♦ 2 number cubes

Mice Multiplication — Game Board

Name

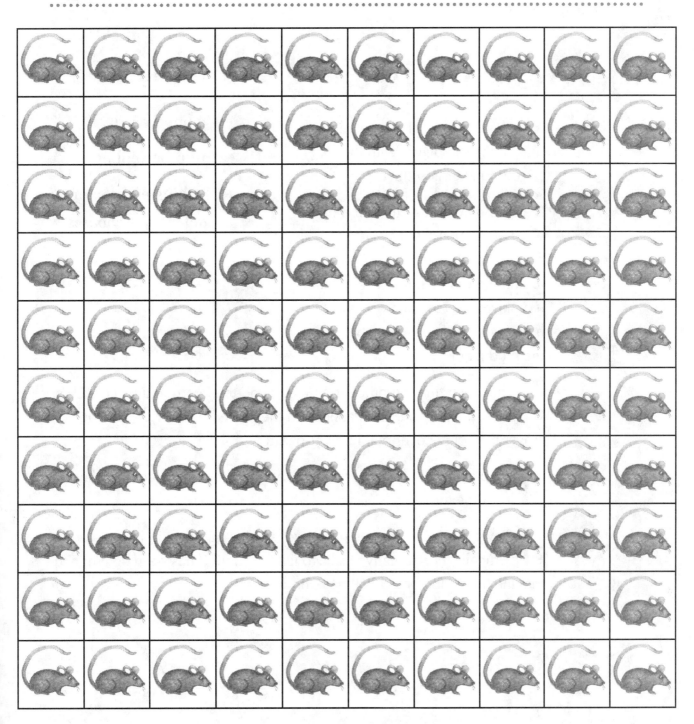

Multiplication Tic-Tac-Toe......2 Players

How to Win   The first player to cover five numbers in a row vertically, horizontally, or diagonally is the winner.

How To Play

What You Need

- 1 game board
- 2 number cubes
- 20 chips per player (*each player chooses one color*)

1 Players each roll one number cube. The player with the largest number goes first.

2 The players take turns rolling two number cubes and multiplying the numbers together to find the product. (For example, if a player rolls a 6 and a 2, they multiply the numbers together to get the product of 12.)

3 They then find the product on the tic-tac-toe board and place a chip over it. (Some numbers appear on the game board twice, but the player may only cover one number per turn.)

4 If a player rolls a number that has already been covered, the player loses the turn.

5 Play continues until one player covers five numbers in a row vertically, horizontally, or diagonally, or until it has been determined that the tic-tac-toe board will have no winner.

Multiplication Tic-Tac-Toe Game Board

1	20	3	5	15	8	2	12
9	25	2	24	5	1	30	6
4	5	20	8	36	18	5	15
16	3	10	12	25	5	4	1
24	1	2	18	15	4	16	24
16	36	10	1	12	6	25	1
12	25	1	8	5	12	4	18
18	4	20	3	24	30	6	36

Cookie Quotients

Any number can play

How to Win The player who collects the most chips is the winner.

How to Play

1 Each player takes a game board and rolls one number cube. The player with the largest number goes first.

2 Players take turns rolling two number cubes, finding the sum, and selecting that number of chips.

3 Each player then divides that number of chips evenly between the two cookies, placing the chips directly on top of those pictured on the cookies. If there is one odd chip left over, the player keeps that chip.

4 Play continues until the spaces on each player's cookies are covered with playing chips. Players do not have to have the exact number of chips to go out. For example, if there are two chips left uncovered on the cookies and the player rolls two 6's, she or he may cover the remaining chips and go out.

5 The player with the largest number of the chips left over from the odd numbers rolled is the winner.

What You Need

⬥ game boards
(1 for each player)

⬥ 2 number cubes

⬥ chips

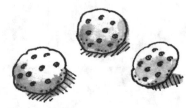

Cookie Quotient

Game Board

Name

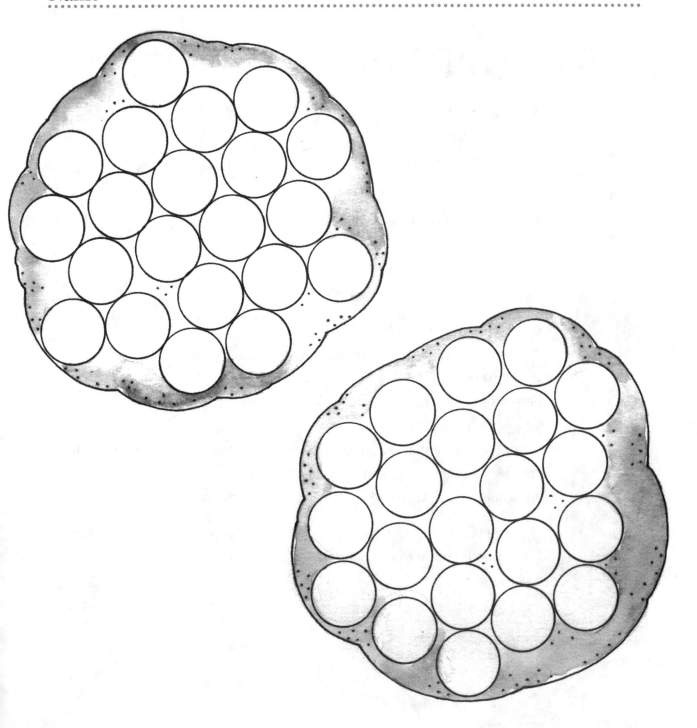

Fraction Action ....2 Players

How to Win The first player to fill a game board with pizza pie pieces is the winner.

How to Play

1 Players place pie-shaped pieces in the paper bag, then decide who will go first.

2 Players take turns rolling the number cube to determine how many pieces to pull from the bag (without looking) and place on their pizza-pie-pan game boards.

3 During a player's turn, a player may rearrange pizza pieces to better fill his or her pie pans. *For example,* if a player pulls a half pie piece from the bag and cannot fit it on any pie pan, she or he can try moving smaller pieces to another pie pan to free some space. If the new piece is too big to fit anywhere, it gets returned to the bag, and it's the next player's turn.

4 The first player to exactly fill the four pizza pie pans on his or her game board with pie pieces is the winner.

What You Need

- ♦ game boards *(1 for each player)*

- ♦ game board pieces *(reproduce 3 sets; glue onto construction paper; let dry and cut apart)*

- ♦ 1 number cube

- ♦ paper bag

Fraction Action

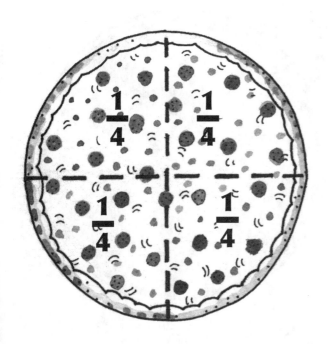

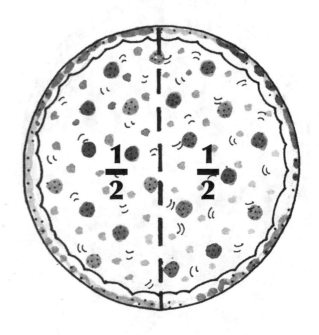

Fraction Action

Name

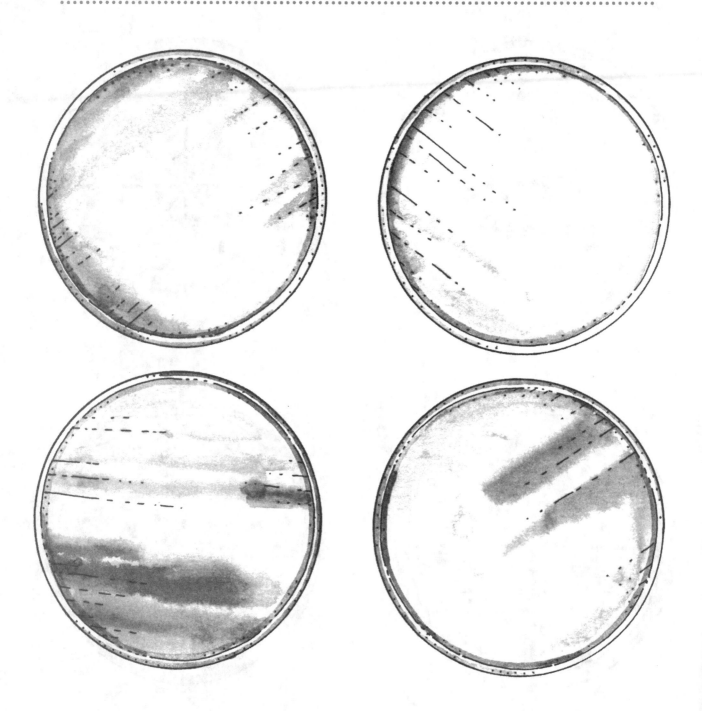

Guess-timation! .... 2 Players

How to Win   The player with the most chips on the turtle is the winner.

How to Play

What You Need

- 1 game board
- 1 number cube
- chips crayons
- container filled with chips

1 Players share one game board. Each player chooses one turtle.

2 Players decide who will go first. Players take turns reaching one hand into the container and trying to pull out 21 chips. (No counting or peeking allowed.)

3 Players take turns throwing the number cube and placing that number of counters down on the turtle's spots. Spots must be covered in numerical order beginning with one.

4 Each player continues playing until he or she covers a turtle or runs out of chips. A player does not have to roll the exact number to finish covering the turtle.

5 Players who have more than 21 chips must count their extra chips and then remove that number of chips from their turtle to get a final total. The player who comes closest to covering 21 spots is the winner.

Another Way to Play   The player who comes closest to 21 without going over is the winner.

Guess-timation !

Game Board

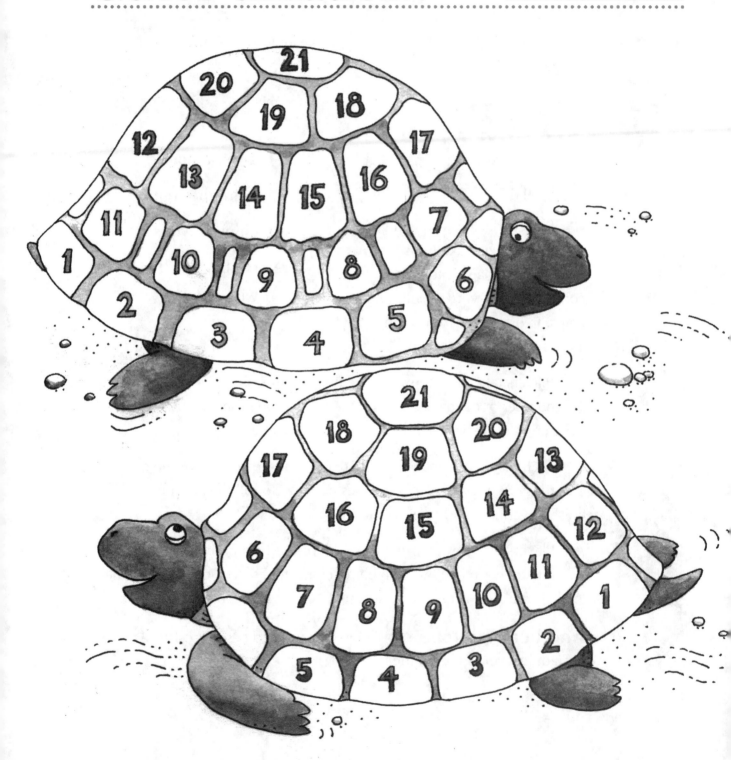

Put on a Happy Face .... Any number can play

How to Win   The first player to draw all of the geometric-shaped parts of a happy face drawing is the winner.

How to Play

1 Each player rolls the number cube. The player with the largest number goes first.

2 Players take turns rolling the cube and drawing all the parts of a happy face as follows: *1 = one circular head, 2 = one triangle ear (players must roll two 2's), 3 = one square eye (players must roll two 3's), 4 = one half-circle mouth, 5 = one rectangle nose, 6 = spiral hair*

3 To begin drawing, a player must first roll a number 1 for the face on which to add the other parts.

4 If a player rolls a number matching a body part that he does not need to add to his face drawing, the player must wait until the next turn to try again.

5 The first player to finish his drawing (complete with all the features listed above) is the winner.

What You Need

❦ drawing paper

❦ 1 number cube

❦ pencils or crayons

Ms. Peabody's Bank

Any number can play

How to Win The first player to have coins totaling $1.00 or more is the winner.

How to Play

1 Each player rolls the number cube. The player with the highest number goes first.

2 Players each select a game board, then decide which color chip will represent pennies and which will represent dimes.

3 Players take turns rolling the number cube and selecting that number of "pennies."

4 Players place the chips representing pennies on the game board so they cover the pennies pictured there.

5 When players collect more than nine pennies, they exchange ten pennies for a "dime." They cover one dime with a chip representing dimes and place any remaining pennies on the penny spots.

6 When a player collects more than nine dimes and nine pennies, he or she has a dollar or more and is declared the winner.

What You Need

❧ game boards *(1 for each player)*

❧ 1 number cube

❧ 2 different-colored chips *(representing pennies and dimes)*

Ms. Peabody's Bank   Game Board

Name

ONE DOLLAR

Carnival Cash

2 to 4 players

How to Win The player with the most money at the end of the game is the winner.

How to Play

1 Each player rolls the number cube. The player with the largest number goes first.

2 Select one player to act as the carnival owner. The carnival owner may also play the game.

3 The carnival owner pays each player $1.00 allowance (four quarters).

4 Each player places a different-colored chip at the start of the game board.

5 Players take turns rolling the number cube, moving forward that number of spaces, and following the directions on that space.

6 During the game, the carnival owner makes any money exchanges as players gain and lose money. If a player runs out of money, he or she is out of the game.

7 Players do not need to roll an exact number to finish the game. When all players have reached the exit, the player who has the most money left is the winner.

What You Need

- game board
- different color chips (*1 color for each player*)
- 1 number cube
- reproducible coins (*pennies, nickles, dimes, quarters*)

Carnival Cash

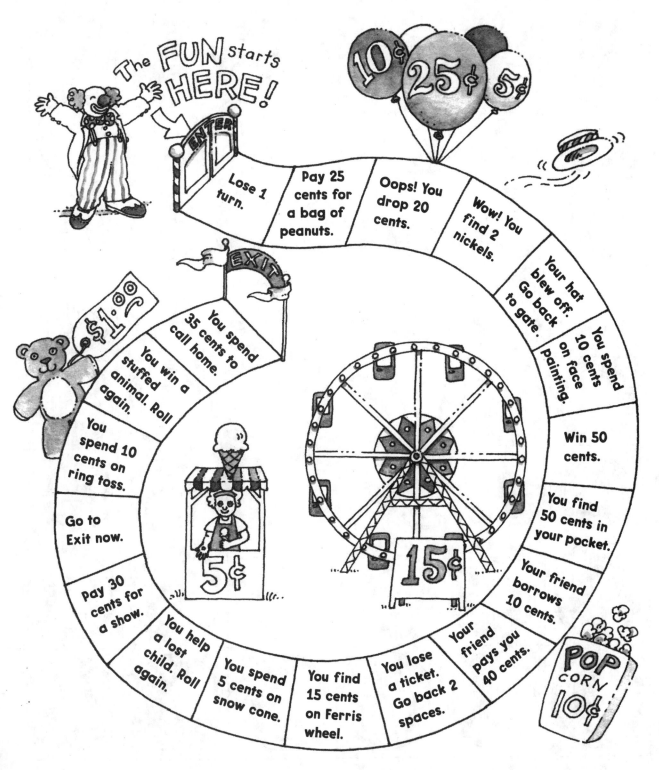

The FUN starts HERE!

ENTER

10¢ 25¢ 5¢

Lose 1 turn.

Pay 25 cents for a bag of peanuts.

Oops! You drop 20 cents.

Wow! You find 2 nickels.

Your hat blew off. Go back to gate.

You spend 10 cents on face painting.

Win 50 cents.

You find 50 cents in your pocket.

Your friend borrows 10 cents.

EXIT

$1.00

You spend 35 cents to call home.

You win a stuffed animal. Roll again.

You spend 10 cents on ring toss.

Go to Exit now.

Pay 30 cents for a show.

You help a lost child. Roll again.

You spend 5 cents on snow cone.

You find 15 cents on Ferris wheel.

You lose a ticket. Go back 2 spaces.

Your friend pays you 40 cents.

5¢

15¢

POP CORN 10¢

Carnival Cash

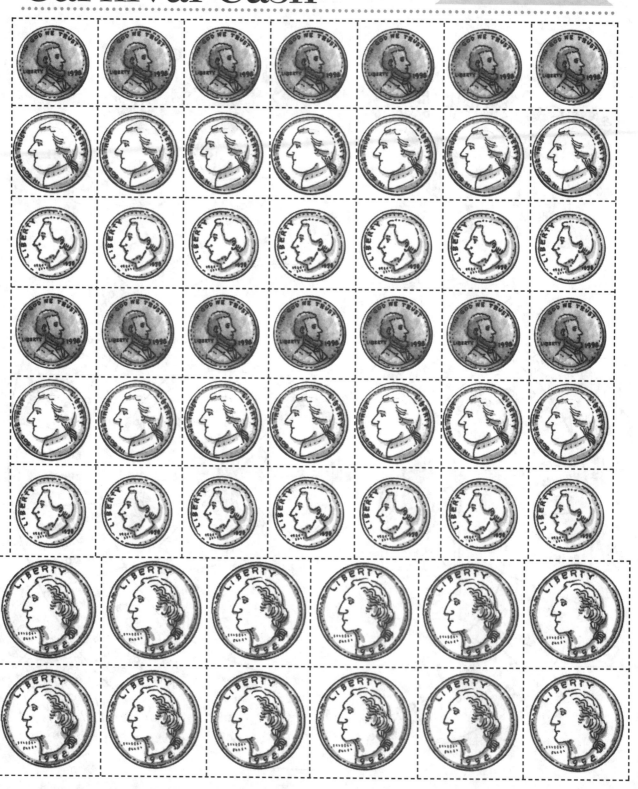

Time Flies! .... 2 Players

How to Win The player with the most elapsed time is the winner.

How to Play

1 Players move paper clock hands to 12 o'clock. Then each player rolls the number cube. The lowest roll goes first.

2 Players take turns rolling the number cube and recording the roll on the record sheet. *For example,* if a player gets 6 for roll one, she or he would add 6 minutes onto 12:00 for a time of 12:06.

3 Players add the number of minutes to the previous time on the record sheet and move the hands on their clock to reflect the new time. Each player must then say the new time aloud. (Example: "My clock says twelve twenty.")

4 Play continues until each player has taken 4 turns. The player with the most time elapsed is the winner.

Another Way to Play The player with the least amount of time elapsed is the winner.

What You Need

- **2 paper clock faces** *(glue to oaktag, then cut apart, attach clock hands to clock face with brass fastener)*
- **record sheet** *(1 for each player)*
- **1 number cube**
- **pencils**

Time Flies!

Name

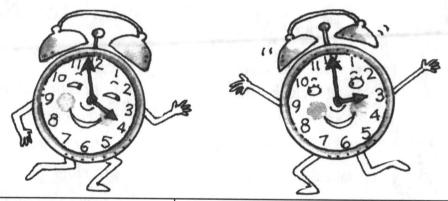

Starting Time	12:00
Roll 1	+ ___ Minutes
New Time	
Roll 2	+ ___ Minutes
New Time	
Roll 3	+ ___ Minutes
New Time	
Roll 4	+ ___ Minutes
Final Time	

Time Flies!

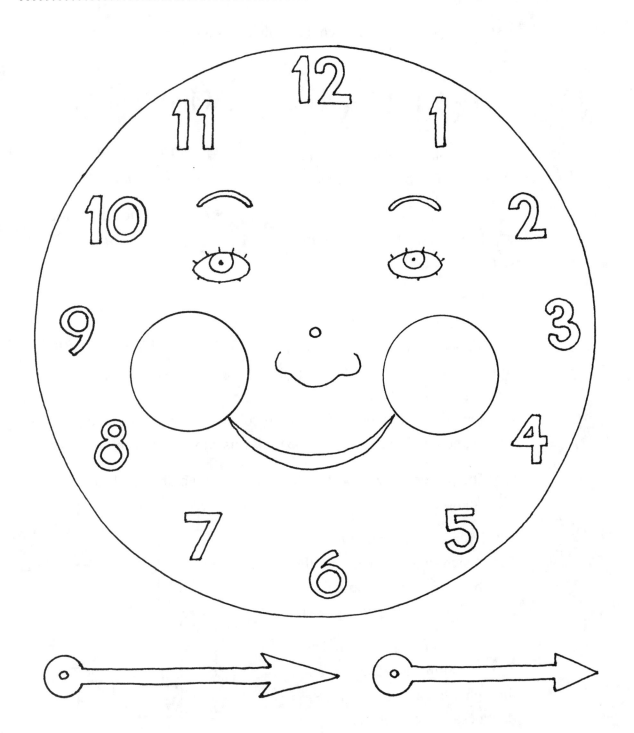

Measure Up

Any number can play

How to Win The first player to reach the doghouse is the winner.

How to Play

What You Need

1 Each player rolls the number cube. The player with the largest number goes first.

2 Players take turns rolling the number cube.

3 Players find START on the game board. They then use their rulers to measure and draw a straight-line segment the number of inches shown on the cube. *For example,* if the number shown on the cube is 4, the measurement of the line segment will be 4 inches. Next, players should color in their path.

4 The players may choose to travel any of the paths that lead to the doghouse.

5 If players are unable to fit a straight-line segment into the maze path because it is too long, they must pass their turn to the next player.

6 The first player to complete measuring and drawing a line through the maze to reach the doghouse is the winner.

- ♣ game boards *(1 for each player)*
- ♣ reproducible rulers *(cut out before playing)*
- ♣ 1 number cube
- ♣ pencils and crayons

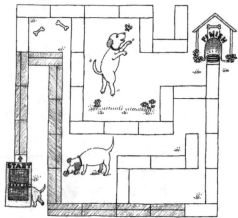

Measure Up

Name

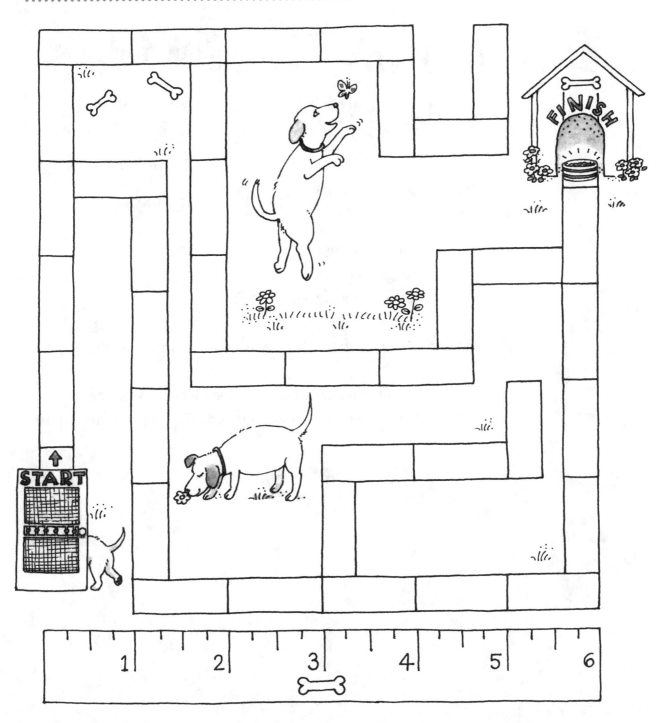

Great Graph Race

Any number can play

How to Win The player who fills in all the blocks beside one number wins.

How to Play

1 Each player rolls one number cube. The player with the largest number goes first.

2 Players each select a game board.

3 Players take turns rolling the number cubes and adding the numbers that appear on the face of the cubes.

4 Players then color one box beside that sum (number) on the graph.

5 Play continues until a player fills in all the blocks beside one of the number columns on his or her game board. That player is the winner.

What You Need

- ❦ game boards *(1 for each player)*
- ❦ 2 number cubes
- ❦ crayons

Great Graph Race

Game Board

Name

2						
3						
4						
5						
6						
7						
8						
9						
10						
11						
12						

Constellation Graph

Any number can play

How to Win   Everyone who plays this game is a winner! Each player plots coordinate points and then creates her or his own "constellation" in the night sky.

How to Play

1 Each player rolls one number cube. The player with the largest number goes first.

2 Players take turns rolling the number cubes. The number on the red cube will represent the x coordinate, and the number on the yellow cube will represent the y coordinate. The players plot points on the game board grid using the two sets of coordinates.

3 Players roll the number cubes 20 times and plot 20 sets of coordinates

4 Players then decide how they will connect their 20 dots so that when connected, the dots resemble a night sky star picture or design.

What You Need

* game boards *(1 for each player)*

* 1 red cube *(represents the X coordinate)*

* 1 yellow cube *(represents the Y coordinate)*

* pencils

* art supplies

Constellation Graph Game Board

Name

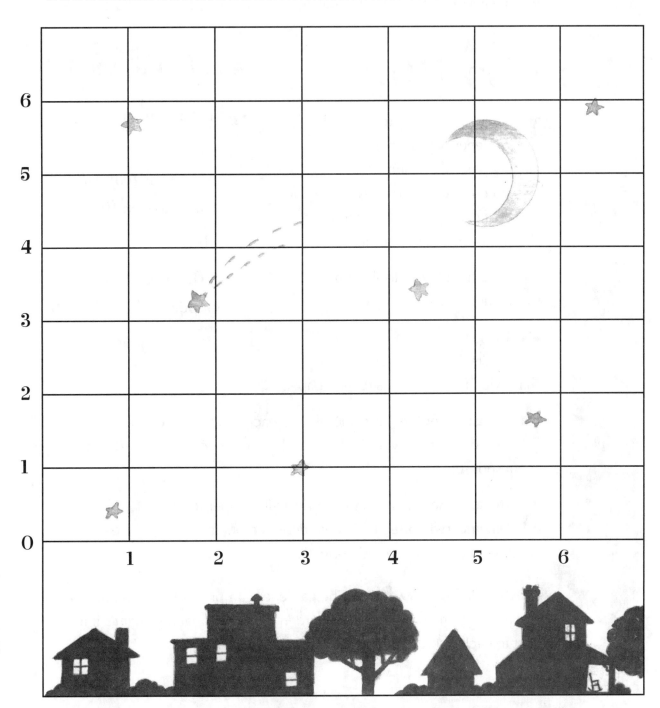

Teaches This Skill
Visual Memory

Forget-Me-Not

3 or more players

How to Win This cooperative game doesn't have a winner. The team of players works together to remember color and number details as arranged on the game board.

How to Play

What You Need

- 1 game board
- Forget-me-not questions (*copied & cut apart on line*)
- chips
- 1 sheet construction paper

1 Select one player to act as the gardener. The gardener secretly places any number of colored chips on the circles in the center of each flower. The gardener also holds the list of questions.

2 All other players look at the garden scene for 10 seconds.

3 The gardener then carefully covers the game board and the chips with a sheet of construction paper.

4 The gardener then asks the players each of the six questions, and records their answer. Players should work *together* to decide on one response.

5 The gardener then lifts the construction paper to see if the players remembered correctly. The gardener colors in a flower for each question that was answered correctly.

Another Way to Play The gardener can privately ask the players to answer the same questions. The gardener then jots each student's initials next to each question answered correctly.

Forget-Me-Not

Game Board

Questions

1 What color chip covers the flower face with glasses? _____

2 What color chip covers the tallest flower face? _____

3 What color chip covers the sleepy flower face? _____

4 What color chip covers the shortest flower face? _____

5 What color chip covers the sad flower face? _____

6 Name the colors of the chips on the flower faces from left to right. _____
_____

Button, Button.........................2 Players

How to Win The first person to correctly guess the secret button card the other player has face down wins.

How to Play

What You Need

- ♦ game boards *(1 for each player)*
- ♦ 1 set of game cards *(made by copying the game board & cutting the cards apart. Players may use crayons to color buttons thus adding a color element to the game)*

1 Each player takes a game board. Players decide who will go first. Shuffle the button cards and place them face down in a pile. Each player takes one card, looks at it, and places it face down.

2 Players take turns asking each other one question that can be answered "yes" or "no" only. *For example:* "Is my button round?" If answer is "yes" player puts chips on her or his game board on all buttons that are not round.

3 Anytime during her or his turn, a player may try to guess the secret button card. If a player guesses incorrectly, player loses a turn.

4 The first player to correctly guess the secret button card the other player is hiding is the winner.

Another Way to Play A third player may act as the "button holder" by picking one button card for two other players to guess.

Button, Button

Game Board

Name

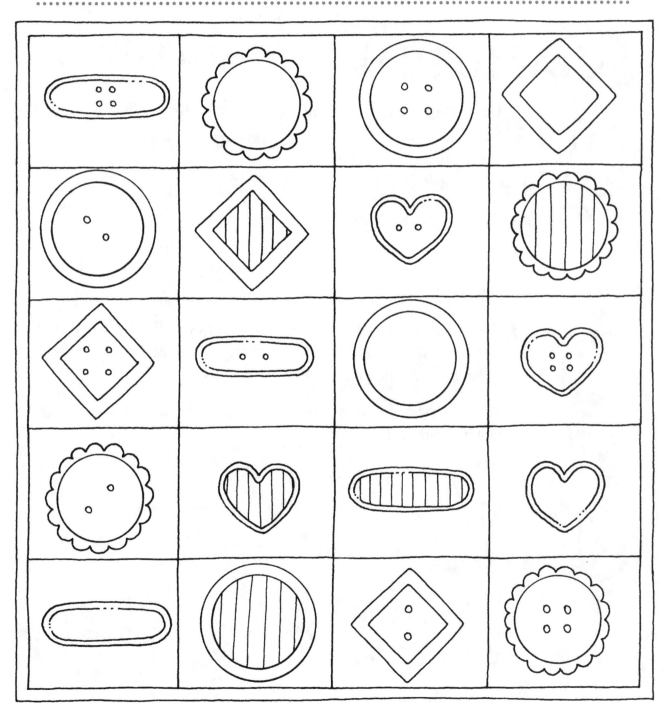

Spider Trap ....

2 or more players

How to Win The player who has the most chips at the end of the game is the winner

How to Play

1 Cover the circles on the game board with 32 chips, leaving the center circle empty. Players decide who will go first.

2 Players take turns jumping over chips into empty spaces. When a player jumps over a chip, the chip is removed from the board and becomes the property of the player who jumped it.

3 Players may jump only one chip at a time; however, he or she may make multiple jumps provided that there is an empty space between chips and it follows the lines on the board.

4 Play ends when no more jumps are possible; the winner is the player with the most chips.

What You Need

- 1 game board
- 32 chips

Spider Trap

Game Board

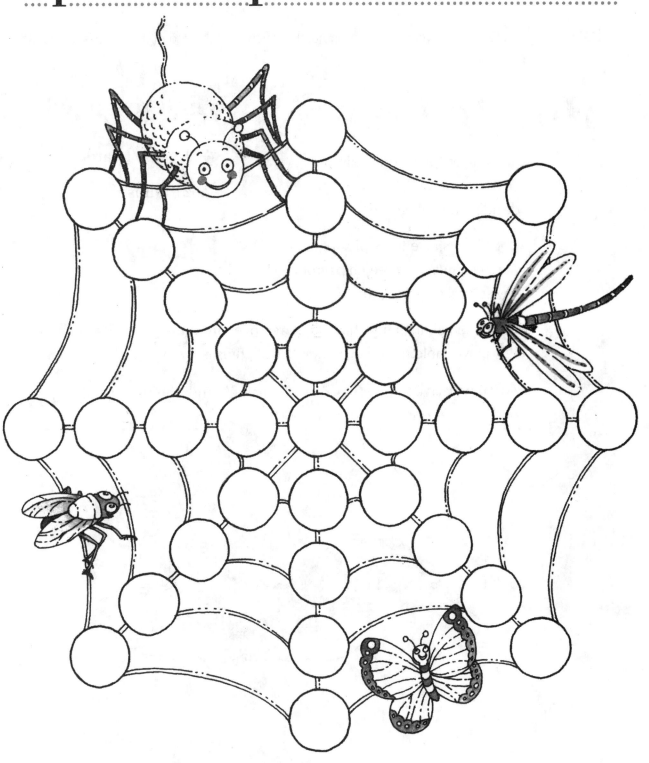

C $ ⊙ >

**Teaches
This Skill**
Logical
Reasoning

C $ ⊙ <

Get Even! .... 2 Players

How to Win The player with the even number of chips at the end of the game is the winner.

How to Play

1 Players place one chip on each of the 21 spaces, then decide who will go first.

2 Players take turns picking up one, two, or three chips from any spaces on the board.

3 When all the chips have been removed from the game board, the player holding the even number of chips is the winner.

Another Way to Play At the game's end, the player holding the odd number of chips is the winner.

What You Need

⬙ 1 game board

⬙ 21 chips

Get Even!

Notes

Notes

Notes

Notes

Notes

Notes

Notes